DEVELOP
DELAY

C000110028

Pamela Bartram
and Sue and Jim Clifford

Published by
CoramBAAF Adoption and Fostering Academy
41 Brunswick Square
London WC1N 1AZ
www.corambaaf.org.uk

Coram Academy Limited, registered as a company limited by
guarantee in England and Wales number 9697712, part of the
Coram group, charity number 312278

Originally printed by BAAF in 2013.
Reprinted by CoramBAAF in 2017

British Library Cataloguing in Publication Data
A catalogue record for this book is available from the British Library

ISBN 978 1 907585 70 8

Project management by Jo Francis, Publications Department,
CoramBAAF
Designed and typeset by Fravashi Aga
Printed in Great Britain by the Lavenham Press
Trade distribution by Turnaround Publisher Services, Unit 3,
Olympia Trading Estate, Coburg Road, London N22 6TZ

Contents

Acknowledgements

Sincere thanks to Rita and Cheryl for offering their time and insight and my warm thanks to Dr Deborah Hodes, Consultant Paediatrician, for her help with definitions.

Notes about the authors

Pamela Bartram grew up in Glasgow, studied Indian Philosophy and went on to train as a music therapist, working with profoundly disabled children. Subsequently, she retrained as a child psychotherapist, to engage with children in different ways and in the context of the family as a whole. Now also an adult psychotherapist, she works as a clinician/manager in the NHS, developing and managing a CAMHS team for disabled children and their families, and in private practice with children, adolescents and adults. She has a special interest in work with parents and in supporting the process of psychological change where a condition is "incurable".

Sue and Jim Clifford, inspired by Jim's own successful adoption, have since 1990 adopted nine children, aged between four and ten on placement. The story of their youngest, and the therapeutic parenting model they use to turn their children's lives around, was told in the much-acclaimed BBC documentary, screened in 2011, 'A Home for Maisie'. Both parents are well known as speakers on adoption and parenting challenging children. Sue, a dyslexia specialist, is an Adoption UK parent-buddy, and runs parenting training courses. Jim is a corporate financier, and an academic researcher at Cass Business School. He is the author of a study on the impact of permanence in adoption and fostering, and has developed, with the Consortium of Voluntary Adoption Agencies, the first adoption social impact bond for hard-to-place children.

The series editor

The editor of this series, **Hedi Argent**, is an established author/editor for BAAF. Her books cover a wide range of family placement topics; she has written several guides and a story book for young children.

Looking behind the label...

Jack has mild learning difficulties and displays some characteristics of ADHD and it is uncertain whether this will increase...

Beth and Mary both have a diagnosis of global developmental delay...

Abigail's birth mother has a history of substance abuse. There is no clear evidence that Abigail was prenatally exposed to drugs but her new family will have to accept some kind of developmental uncertainty...

Jade has some literacy and numeracy difficulties, but has made some improvement with the support of a learning mentor...

Prospective adopters and carers are often faced with the prospect of having to decide whether they can care for a child with a health need or condition they know little about and have no direct experience of. No easy task...

Will Jack's learning difficulties become more severe?
Will Beth and Mary be able to catch up?
When will it be clear whether or not Abigail has been affected by parental substance misuse?
And will Jade need a learning mentor throughout her school life?

It can be difficult to know where to turn for reliable information. What lies behind the diagnoses and "labels" that many looked after children bring with them? And what will it be like to live with them? How will they benefit from family life?

Parenting Matters is a unique series, "inspired" by the terms used – and the need to "decode them" – in profiles of children needing new permanent families. Each title provides expert knowledge about a particular condition, coupled with facts, figures and guidance presented in a straightforward and accessible style. Each book also describes what it is like to parent an affected child, with adopters and foster carers "telling it like it is", sharing their parenting experiences, and offering useful advice; some of these cases are more recent than others, and it is useful to remember that professional practice in the past is not what it is today. This combination of expert information and first-hand experiences will help readers to gain understanding, and to make informed decisions.

Titles in the series deal with a wide range of health conditions and steer readers to where they can get more information. They offer a sound introduction to the topic under consideration and offer a glimpse of what it would be like to live with a "labelled" child. Most importantly, this series looks behind the label and gives families the confidence to look more closely at a child whom they otherwise might have passed by.

Keep up with those titles already published or new titles by signing up to our newsletter on www.baaf.org.uk/bookshop.

Shaila Shah
CoramBAAF Publisher

Titles in this series include:

- *Parenting a Child with Attention Deficit Hyperactivity Disorder*

- *Parenting a Child with Dyslexia*

- *Parenting a Child with Mental Health Issues*

- *Parenting a Child Affected by Parental Substance Misuse*

- *Parenting a Child with Emotional and Behavioural Difficulties*

- *Parenting a Child with Autism Spectrum Disorder*

Introduction

This book is concerned with developmental delay and the special needs of children, particularly adopted and fostered children, who have this difficulty.

The first half of the book starts with an explanation of developmental delay and what this term means for children: symptoms and prognoses are outlined clearly and simply. It goes on to look at the different ways in which developmental delay can affect child development; the stresses that this issue can cause in the surrounding family; and the likely outcomes for children affected by developmental delay.

The second half of the book tells the story of Sue and Jim Clifford and their experience of parenting children with developmental delay, and how this affected day-to-day family life.

UNDERSTANDING DEVELOPMENTAL DELAY

PAMELA BARTRAM

CHAPTER 1

Developmental delay

Francis is 14 years old. He walks unsteadily and wears a helmet to protect his head when a seizure causes him to fall. He has some echolalic speech. He likes to sit and rock back and forth, making a high-pitched humming sound. He enjoys playing with a pop-up animal toy and does this repeatedly. He flicks the pages of books but doesn't look at the pictures. He is not interested in watching television for longer than a few minutes at a time, but loves to travel in the car. Francis sleeps deeply; he enjoys a good range of foods and eats heartily.

Joanna is 15 months old. She has been taken into care because her birth parents were unable to look after her. She is a sociable little girl, eager for adult attention. Joanna can sit unsupported and is just beginning to pull herself up to stand. She doesn't have any words yet. She eats well but sleeps badly, waking during the night crying. When presented with toys, she holds them briefly and then throws them, usually behind her.

Mohammed is five years old and has Down's Syndrome. He likes to play with dolls and action figures. In one game, the baby doll always falls on his head. Mohammed calls that doll "baby all gone". Mohammed pushes other children and has bitten his younger brother more than once. He can speak in short sentences and tries hard to play football although his co-ordination is immature. Mohammed's parents say he is a fussy eater and he doesn't like to sit at the table at mealtimes.

All of these children can be described as developmentally delayed, although they are very different from each other, with individual characteristics and abilities.

What is developmental delay?

The term "developmental delay" is used to describe children whose skills and abilities, for many possible reasons, are not developing as expected. These skills and abilities may include:

- fine and gross motor skills;

- thinking, reasoning and remembering skills;

- language and communication skills;

- social skills;

- sensory processing skills;

- hearing and vision.

A child who is described as "developmentally delayed" may have difficulties in some or all of those areas, and to varying degrees. Whereas the term "global developmental delay" indicates delay in all aspects of development, a specific developmental problem may well leave other areas of development unaffected.

The description "developmental delay", when given as a diagnosis by a paediatrician, is usually applied to babies and pre-school children. It is predicated on the idea of developmental "milestones" which, in the course of normal development, are reached at or around a certain age. For example, a typically developing baby might be expected to sit unaided between six and nine months, or to say single words between 14 and 18 months, and to walk steadily at some time between 15 and 18 months. The developmentally delayed child, however, may either reach these milestones later than their typically developing peers, or in some cases, not at all.

Some clinicians stress the importance of considering what is the norm for any particular family before judging a child's development to be delayed, as developmental milestones are reached by individual children within individual families. They also talk about periods of uncertainty, during which it may be unclear whether or not parents should be concerned about delay in development (McInley and Holland, 1986, p. 29). It is important then to monitor development over a period of time.

However, in some cases it is quite evident that developmental delay is present and this may be linked to a particular and identifiable condition.

Case study: James

James has a diagnosis of Noonan Syndrome and Hypertrophic cardiomyopathy. Noonan Syndrome is a genetically caused and congenital (present at the time of birth) disorder, a type of dwarfism, which affects learning ability and is associated with certain facial features and restricted height. Hypertrophic cardiomyopathy is a feature of Noonan Syndrome and is a heart condition that can cause breathlessness, pain and fainting. At the age of two, James has a significant hearing impairment and is delayed in both his communication and level of understanding compared with other children of his age. He is described as a very "loud" child who does not need much sleep. He only eats sweets and finger foods; he is very active, with challenging behaviours, and requires constant supervision. His mother finds his behaviour difficult to deal with. Although she sets boundaries for her other children, she does not set the same boundaries for James.

As young children grow and become of school age, the term "developmental delay" may be used less often to describe them. By that time, it may have become clearer that their development is not going to "catch up" with that of their peers. Instead, they have impairments of various kinds, which hopefully will improve with help, but are unlikely ever to resolve altogether. Rather than continuing to be described as developmentally delayed, therefore, children often go on to be described as having a disability – either learning, physical or in the area of "social communication". This transition from being thought of as developmentally delayed to being disabled can be a painful one for parents and carers as it brings with it more of a sense of permanence.

For this reason, some people argue that the term "developmental delay", or developmental impairment, even when applied to babies and young children, is unhelpful as it may foster a false expectation that the child will eventually catch up with their peers, which may not be the case.

What are the causes of developmental delay?

Some babies and children have, from the time of their conception, a genetic or chromosomal disorder where developmental delay is part of the condition. The most commonly occurring chromosomal disorder is Down's Syndrome, which is caused by the presence of all or part of an extra chromosome, number 21. Other chromosomal disorders include Fragile X and Noonan Syndrome (see the case study of James, above). Autism is a condition that affects many aspects of a child's development, and it is currently thought that specific genes are affected; the hope is that these will eventually be fully identifiable.

Where a specific condition can be identified, parents and carers can access information about the likely prognosis for the child, notwithstanding individual variation between different children. If they want to, they can also have an explanation about what has happened in the child's genetic make-up that has resulted in the developmental delay. One important consideration for parents and carers is the likelihood of the same condition occurring in another baby, and genetic counselling can offer information and guidance. This is, of course, of importance to birth parents who may be planning to have another baby, but could also be important for foster carers or adopters if they might consider caring for more children from the same family.

Unlike these conditions, which are present in the genetic make-up of the baby and child, some causes of developmental delay are infections acquired either *in utero*, or around the time of birth or after birth. For example, the baby may be infected by rubella *in utero*, if the mother comes into contact with rubella (also called German measles), and this can cause deafness and blindness as well as cognitive disability in the baby. Postnatally, a baby or young child may contract meningitis or encephalitis, which can leave their development severely affected. Physical trauma as well as infections can cause an acquired condition: lack of oxygen during the birth process can cause cerebral palsy, where many areas of development are adversely affected. Any injury to the brain, whether accidental or non-accidental, as in the case of physical abuse, can be another cause of developmental delay. Babies *in utero* can also be affected by the mother's drug or alcohol misuse, which may have long-lasting effects on the child's development and well-being.

When I talk to my colleagues in the child development team where I work, I find that in most of the cases we see of children with developmental delay, the cause is, in fact, unexplained. Sometimes it is simply the case that, for no known reason, a baby's milestones are delayed and no underlying condition is ever identified to explain it. Different parents and carers respond to this in different ways. For some, the search for a cause can become very important. For others, there can be relief in having no defined cause, as this leaves room for optimism about the child's potential to develop.

The impact of environmental deprivation

Perhaps it is of particular relevance to foster carers and adoptive parents that children who have experienced deprivation in the early months and years of their lives may well be developmentally delayed. It has been demonstrated that children who were emotionally deprived in the pre-school years failed to put on weight and thrive physically, and showed signs of passivity and delay in development. Once their environment was changed, they showed an accelerated rate of growth (Polnay and Hull, 1985, p. 39). Poor nutrition, mental or physical illness and depression in the child's primary carers can also result in what Polnay and Hull call a "failure to rear", that is to say, what they consider to be the most common cause and the real meaning of the better known "failure to thrive" (Polnay and Hull, 1985, p. 162).

Other research has shown that children raised in institutions or who pass through a series of foster homes have poor language development, poor school attainment and an impaired ability to form emotional attachments (Polnay and Hull, 1985, p. 38).

This raises the question of whether some of the damage coming from environmental causes might be reversible once the child is settled in a home where the care is stable and "good enough". It seems important that families who are thinking about fostering or adopting a child presenting with developmental delay should approach the situation hopefully. However, it would be unwise to assume that any damage sustained previously can be reversed. An adoptive parent of an 18-month-old child with developmental delay may find over time that they are parenting a child who has a lifelong disability, such as a learning disability, physical disability or social communication disability, or a combination of all three.

Other conditions

Children who have developmental delay or a disability may also have other conditions alongside the primary difficulty – this is also called "co-morbidity". Attention deficit hyperactivity disorder (ADHD) is one such condition (see *Parenting a Child with Attention Deficit Hyperactivity Disorder*, in this series (Jacobs and Miles, 2012)).

It is also the case that children with a disability are more likely to have emotional, behavioural or mental health problems. Emerson and Hatton (2007) report that 36 per cent of children and adolescents aged 5–16 with learning disabilities have a distinguishable psychiatric disorder – a rate about six times higher than that of their peers.

CHAPTER **2**

Assessment, diagnosis and trauma

Assessment and diagnosis

The assessment and diagnosis of developmental delay is complex, may take some time and involve a number of tests and several medical practitioners. Assessment may take place before or at the time of the child's birth (e.g. if the baby is discovered to have an identifiable disorder such as Down's Syndrome, or if the baby is very premature or has associated medical problems), or it may take place at a later stage. The timing of assessments will depend on the cause of the developmental delay and may result in the diagnosis of a specific medical condition. Sometimes, however, the cause of the developmental delay may remain unexplained.

Early diagnosis

Mothers are particularly emotionally vulnerable in the period during and after giving birth. It cannot be other than an unwelcome shock to find that the hoped-for perfect baby has not after all arrived. Instead, there may be a baby with physical characteristics that are difficult to come to terms with; urgent medical interventions may be required; or the introduction of a totally unexpected diagnosis has to be taken in and understood both mentally and also emotionally digested.

Samir

Samir was diagnosed with a genetic condition known as Beckworth-Weidermann Syndrome a week after his birth. Tests during pregnancy had not brought any sign to light of this condition, which affects one in 15,000 babies. The syndrome causes overgrowth of organs and limbs. Samir was born with a large tongue, abdominal defects, tumours and "uneven growth" of the lower limbs.

Samir's early care was provided by children's hospital services and four different departments were involved: Speech and Language Therapy, Feeding Clinic, Genetics and Ophthalmology. He needed an operation on his tongue to reduce its size, because it affected his breathing and feeding. Samir's mother was understandably very shocked by his diagnosis; in fact, she became depressed and overwhelmed by worry about the future. On his release from hospital, Samir was placed in foster care. Although his condition did not necessarily mean that he would be cognitively delayed, at the age of nine months he had only just begun to explore with his hands and to put them into his mouth. It was important that his carer stimulated him by talking, smiling and cuddling him as well as by introducing opportunities for him to socialise with other babies in playgroups. Samir's mother could not look after him and he remained in foster care.

Emma

Emma suffered lack of oxygen during the process of her birth. It was later demonstrated that she had been developing normally *in utero* and that the lack of oxygen, which caused brain damage, was due to the negligence of the medical professionals involved. Emma

13

was diagnosed with cerebral palsy. All aspects of her development were severely affected by her condition and her life expectancy was reduced because of her complex difficulties.

Later diagnosis

Sometimes, however, it is not at birth but later that delay in development becomes obvious. For instance, a baby may not reach out for toys, roll over or sit unsupported within the expected timeframe. These may turn out to be early signs of delay in motor development and sometimes also cognitive development.

In other cases, development may appear to be proceeding quite normally until the age when infants would be expected to start to develop speech and language. Children who go on to have a diagnosis of autism spectrum disorder (ASD) are most commonly initially identified through a delay in their language development, which may be picked up between approximately 18 months and two years of age. A child may then first be seen by a speech and language therapist. If she is worried that he has a developmental disorder, which pervades many aspects of his development and not only his language, she will probably refer him to a multi-disciplinary child development team for a more thorough assessment.

For parents and carers, assessment and diagnosis can be a very stressful process and a difficult time. When a child's speech and language development is delayed, parents and carers will often be told by friends and family that children all develop at their own rate and there is nothing to be worried about. It can therefore come as a shock to be told that the child has a lifelong condition, which will manifest itself in a number of ways, with communication, play and imagination all possibly affected.

Variation in how well diagnosis is made

It is to be hoped that assessment and diagnosis are handled sensitively by the professionals involved, but of course, in stressful and painful situations there is always variation in how smoothly the procedures go.

It can take time to digest and process the news that a baby or young child has a serious condition. An adoptive mother of a young child newly diagnosed with an autism spectrum disorder used to have a recurring dream in which her child spoke to her and played with her "like a normal child". This dream seemed to be an expression of her deep wish for her child to be well and to develop normally. It took a long time for her to adjust to the reality of her little girl's developmental difficulties.

Appointments and testing

Any parent or carer of a young child whose development is not proceeding as hoped will have to bear the anxiety and uncertainty inevitably associated with this. They will also have to have enough stamina to deal with the practical demands of looking after a child who may need numerous medical appointments, tests and assessments.

It is interesting but upsetting to see how difficult it can be for professionals to think about the whole child who is also part of a whole family. I have written elsewhere about the way in which children with developmental difficulties are sometimes thought about in separate "bits", as if to think of them as a whole child is too challenging, and perhaps too painful (Bartram, 2009). As we saw above, in the case of Samir, different "parts" of him were attended to by different hospital departments. Whilst there are no doubt sound medical reasons for this, having to relate to so many professionals, who unfortunately do not always successfully relate to each other, can put a strain on parents and carers. Those who do not feel strong enough to co-ordinate their child's medical appointments can easily feel overwhelmed and disempowered.

In *Evidence Based Paediatrics and Child Health*, Drs Salt and Gringas report that the number of tests ordered for a three-year-old child with moderate developmental delay ranged from 0 to 15 and included 26 different investigations (2004, p. 117). Whether you are the parent of the child where no test was ordered, or of the child where 15 tests were ordered, or anywhere in between, it is likely that this will place a strain on you. Depending on what is entailed by the test, probably the child too will be placed under strain. Some children become very distressed when brought for appointments, as they have come to associate seeing professionals with stress, or even physical pain.

Emotional trauma

The word "trauma" comes from the Greek word meaning "to pierce". The idea of a traumatic experience therefore is one which "pierces" our normal self-protective coping mechanisms, and overwhelms us. The psychological effects of these experiences cannot be relied on to stop when the experience stops, but may continue to reverberate until they are alleviated by some special attention or intervention. Whether at the time of assessment, diagnosis, or later as life continues, children and families where there is developmental delay and persistent disability are vulnerable to emotional trauma. One parent described to me the moment when the head teacher of her child's school caught up with her at the bus stop and told her that she thought her daughter was autistic. Had this ever occurred to her? The mother said that this moment remained fixed in her mind, repeating itself over and over again, and always accompanied by the sense that she had been assaulted, left wounded and that she was falling into a black hole. At anniversaries or times of unreached milestones, trauma, which had receded, may be re-awakened.

Sometimes trauma is not a dramatic event, but a quiet accumulation of indigestible disappointment and pain. This can be true for children and young people as well as for their parents and carers.

Case study: Carrie

Carrie had struggled all her life to keep up with her peers in a mainstream setting. She had a facial disfigurement, and thought and behaved in many ways like a child three or four years younger than her classmates. She told her therapist that she wished there was an x-ray machine that could look into her brain and see exactly what was wrong with her. Her daily experience of looking, acting and feeling different had a cumulative effect on her sense of herself and her value. She could not shake off the idea that she was made "all wrong".

CHAPTER **3**

The whole child

It is a truism to say that every child is an individual and should be thought about as such. However, it is also true to say that sometimes where there is damage, a condition or syndrome, it can be tempting to lay everything at the door of the condition rather than to think about the child as a whole.

Ryan was diagnosed with an autism spectrum disorder at the age of two-and-a-half. At nursery, he pushed other children and sometimes bit them. This was attributed to his autism, and the nursery staff urgently requested specialist advice on "behaviour management". There are, of course, many children with an autism spectrum disorder who do not push and bite other children, and equally there are typically developing children who do. In my view, it is important not to attribute everything a child does to her medically diagnosed condition.

I asked Tina, who fostered Kieran, a young person with delay in many areas of his development, what she had understood about his difficulties before he came to live with her. Tina said, 'Well, you see, there is the disability and then there's the child'. She told me that she had read 'all the papers about him, but you have to make your own assessment. The doctors make *their* assessment, but *you* have to make *your own* assessment.'

Tina went on to tell me how she took time to get to know Kieran. Not just know *about* him, but *know* him. The value of getting to know a child for himself or herself should not need spelling out. Yet, where disability is involved, it does seem necessary to emphasise this. Perhaps our anxieties are so stirred up by whatever difficulties are present that we cannot easily allow ourselves to look at the whole child.

In thinking about the whole child, in addition to their physical health, it is helpful to consider five dimensions:

- the personality of the child;
- her stage of development in terms of the lifespan;
- her areas of developmental delay and developmental strengths;
- her emotional well-being and mental health; and
- her environmental influences and life experiences.

These factors will interplay and contribute to the individuality of any child or young person.

Perhaps a sixth dimension could be added, an X factor, something uniquely about the feel or sense of a child, which it seems cannot be accounted for by the other five dimensions.

It may be useful here to say more about the developmental stages across the life span.

Developmental stages across the lifespan

Children with developmental delay, like all children, will pass through stages of emotional and psychological development across the lifespan. Each stage of development may bring its own challenges, as is the case for any child.

The human lifespan can be thought of in terms of six stages, which each have their own characteristic quality:

- infancy

- toddlerhood

- latency

- adolescence

- adulthood

- old age

How development is negotiated in the context of the child's primary relationships in any one stage will be affected by what has gone before, although new stages of development also offer new opportunities to re-work what has gone wrong or remains unresolved from an earlier stage of development.

Infancy

Infancy is characterised by dependency: the baby is entirely dependent on her caregivers for her well-being and for survival itself. At this stage of development, the caregiver can feel at times that they have lost their own identity, so taken up are they by the needs of the helpless infant, both day and night. As the baby moves through infancy, her primary relationship, usually with her mother, expands to allow the inclusion of other important family members – father, siblings and members of the extended family.

Toddlerhood

In toddlerhood, the young child begins to develop a sense of agency and autonomy, hopefully still within the safety of a secure relationship with caregivers. This is the age at which toilet training takes place, language develops, and tantrums, when the child doesn't get "her own way", come to the fore. This can be a taxing stage of development, especially if the caregiver is not comfortable with being challenged or finds the feeling of being out of control particularly difficult to manage. Caregivers can also feel frustrated,

SECTION 1

21

angry and "driven to the end of their tether" at this stage of development, when the young child may insist 'ME do it' long before she has the skills and ability to actually perform the task in question, for example, tying her own shoelaces.

Latency

In the latency period, emotional and psychological development calm and settle. Children start school and become invested in conforming and being "good". They may develop an interest in games which have rules attached to them that must be followed in the interests of fairness and rightness. They may collect cards or dolls, and otherwise occupy themselves with non-aggressive acquisitive pursuits.

Adolescence

Adolescence can be thought of as the psychological response to the onset of puberty, which involves hormonal and physiological changes. In adolescence, many of the characteristics of toddlerhood are revisited, but now the body in question is not that of a two-year-old who can be, if necessary, picked up and carried away screaming. Now the young person is also engaged in discovering and asserting their independence and autonomy but, like the toddler, the adolescent is not yet ready to manage without the guidance and intervention of her parents and carers. This can lead to situations where, at one moment, the young person is asserting their right to make their own decisions, and at the next moment, may be making it necessary for adults to step in and provide clear boundaries. Like toddlerhood, adolescence is a time of great conflict, especially about whether, and how, to separate from parent figures, a conflict that starts within the individual child or young person but easily gets transferred to the parent/child relationship.

Adulthood

Adulthood is a time of greater separateness, when young

people can allow themselves to build a life within which their own new relationships and tasks take precedence over the original family unit.

Old age

In the last stage of life, old age, hopefully we are able to reap the benefits of the life lived, and get ready eventually to let go, and to die.

As we have seen, children who have developmental delay will be delayed in one or more aspects of their development, for example, their speech and language, motor skills, social skills or thinking and reasoning skills. However, this does not mean that they are not also moving through the stages of lifespan development outlined above. These broad developmental stages can provide a useful way of thinking about children's emotional and psychological development.

Case study: Aaron

With the onset of puberty, Aaron, who had moderate learning difficulties, became increasingly aggressive to his family members and in particular to his adoptive mother. She had always been dedicated to looking after him and making sure he had the best possible help. She had given up her career when he was young, because his father travelled for his job and it was essential that one of them was available to take Aaron to appointments, therapies and just to be there for him as much as possible. She was very hurt and shocked when Aaron started to reject her and even at times attack her physically. Unconsciously, she had gone on thinking of him as her "baby" who would never grow up.

When she was able to think about his behaviour in terms of his developmental stage of life, she could see that in some sense his rejection of her was normal. This, of course, is not to suggest that his means of expressing it was either "normal" or acceptable. Nevertheless, it forced her to face the reality of the changes taking place in Aaron's body and mind. This in turn made her look into ways in which his social circle might expand, and ultimately ways in which there might be a plan for him eventually to live separately from the rest of the family, in a normal developmental step. If Aaron had remained in the latency phase of development, causing little disturbance, his mother and he might have found themselves locked forever in a relationship that allowed little room for growth for either of them.

Thinking and feeling

Another common, and in my view unhelpful, way of thinking about children and young people with developmental delay is to attribute any difficult behaviour to "not understanding what he is doing" or "not understanding the consequences of his actions". This way of thinking minimises the child's emotional life by focusing on his perceived cognitive limitations. Indeed, I think that as a society we find it difficult to imagine that children with developmental difficulties have an emotional life at all. Perhaps it is too painful to imagine. Instead, we over-stress the question of understanding, as if understanding is somehow divorced from feeling. In the specialist service where I work, children with developmental difficulties are often referred because of their "behaviour", and there is rarely a reference made to their emotional life, or feelings, as if feelings do not underlie much of their behaviour. I wonder whether society defends itself from thinking about people with developmental problems as having a subjective life, of being people like us, rather than "non people" who are made of different stuff from the rest of us?

Case study: Vincent

Vincent is a teenager who comes to talk to me in my professional capacity from time to time. These are some notes I made on a recent meeting.

'He says the thing is that he hasn't made any friends at college, and I feel very moved by his vulnerability. He says he is in a class, and I shouldn't misunderstand him, they are all nice, there's no bullying or anything like that. But he just senses that no one wants to talk to him.

I ask, he senses it? He says yes, he does talk to them, but he can see that they are often not really listening and they look away as if they are thinking about something else and they move away soon if they can. He says he is fine talking to adults; it's his old problem, he says, of talking to people of his own age in groups. Sometimes his class all go out for lunch – "you know – we go out of the college for lunch and sometimes I go too and we are all in a group and I try to talk to them but it doesn't work. It's hard," he says, "looking at a group of people all chatting and talking and not being part of it. It's hard to feel no one cares about you. And it's a two-year course." He could put up with anything for a year but it's two years. I agree and say he feels he doesn't belong and that no one cares about him.

I am struggling with my own feelings of sadness for him, finding it very painful and wishing I could provide a solution. He looks at me with hurt in his eyes, as if to see what I think of him.'

This gives an idea of what Vincent experiences on a daily basis. No one would guess from his behaviour or mild manner that he was sad or troubled.

CHAPTER 4

Stresses and protective factors in the family

Children who have developmental difficulties are naturally more vulnerable than their typically developing peers. Parents and carers have additional stresses too, of both a practical and emotional nature. The children are likely to have an ongoing need for extra care and attention which outlasts that of their peers, and families may struggle with a sense of social isolation, exacerbated by social stigmatisation and by, for example, the very practical matter of inaccessible transportation. There is a higher rate of separation and divorce among the parents of disabled children than in the general population and it is not difficult to see why. Lack of sleep, financial worries – one parent may have to give up their job to care for a child whose development is not going as expected – may all place a strain on the family unit. Worries about the future also play their part even at an early stage in the child's life, as parents and carers find they cannot take for granted that their child will one day have a job, make relationships, marry and be able to live an independent life.

Once the initial assessment and diagnosis are complete, the family may be offered ongoing services from a number of agencies, health, education, social care and the voluntary sector; therapy programmes may be offered to help with speech, movement, sensory difficulties and so on. Although these may be very welcome, having many appointments can interfere with the sense of leading an ordinary life. Life can become medicalised with therapy sessions taking the place of drop-ins or playgroups. Some parents feel they have to be doing "homework" during much of the time they might otherwise have spent playing with their child or taking him out to the park. Careful thought has to be given as to how much therapy and how many therapists and professionals a family can make use of. There has to be a careful balance between the needs of the individual child for whom programmes of exercises may be prescribed and the needs of the whole family, which also has to support, as much as possible, the ordinary needs of a growing child.

It is not unusual to hear parents admit they are confused by the number of people involved in their child's life and unsure as to their roles. At the same time, it is very difficult to turn down any offer of a service, because there is the fear that they might be depriving their child of the best possible chance to develop their abilities.

Some families take what can be thought of as an overactive and somewhat "manic" response to their child's developmental difficulties. New therapies are always sought out and tried; the child has to relate to many professionals and is perhaps confronted with his own limitations too often for his own sense of well-being and autonomy.

Deborah Marks writes:

> *Thus the kind of interdisciplinary practices enacted*
> *upon the physically disabled person (or the person*

with learning difficulties…) are much more intensive
than those imposed upon the "normal"… The
experience, particularly for the infant or young child,
of having things constantly done to them, often by
a series of strangers but with the agreement of a
trusted figure such as a parent, can be disruptive to
their "continuity of being" and therefore traumatic.

(1999, p. 69)

Marks goes on to quote Mason, who says:

Other children play, but you do therapy. Other
children develop but you are "trained". Almost every
activity of daily living can take on the dimension of
trying to make you less like yourself… The world is
often quite happy to reinforce this.

(Marks, 1999, p. 69)

Some families seem to manage to achieve a more reasonable
balance, taking into account the need for the parents to look
after their own relationship, as well as the needs of any other
children in the family.

Research has helped us to understand which families are likely
to cope better than others when bringing up a child with
developmental difficulties.

Parenting and families' indicators for coping

Research has found that supportive relationships within the
nuclear family predicted effective coping. This was broken down

into 'degree of cohesion, degrees of expressiveness, and the presence of active recreation' (Matson and Marchetti, 1988, p. 50). The reference to expressiveness is of particular interest. This suggests that families where people are able to express what they are thinking and feeling, whether positive or negative, are likely to cope better with the challenges of living with a developmentally delayed child than families in which such self-expression is not possible. This would accord with my experience as a psychotherapist, that giving yourself and others permission to have and express a range of feelings is good for mental and emotional health. The reference to active recreation is also helpful and seems to support the idea that families in which therapies take over from real life may not cope as well in the long run as those which achieve a better balance. Too much focus on the developmental problems or on the disability can have a disabling effect on the family itself.

In another piece of research, it was found that marital satisfaction was the 'single best predictor of long-term outcome for the family' (Matson and Marchetti, 1988, p. 50). It was also found that where families received appropriate "formal support", for example, respite care programmes, and informal support from friends and extended family, this support had a good effect on the parents' relationship, which in turn had a good effect on maternal parenting (Matson and Marchetti, 1988, p. 51).

Without these social supports, parents are at risk of feeling isolated and alone with their worries. This is one of the greatest problems for parents of children with developmental difficulties. Sometimes parent support groups are offered, on the premise that parents are likely to feel most supported and understood by other people who are in a similar situation. These can be of great help. However, in my experience foster carers and adopters can be quite reluctant to attend such groups, or if they do, they become acutely sensitive to the differences between themselves and birth parents and between one child and another. Groups can bring people together, but for some, unfortunately, they can serve to underline the experience of feeling alone, and that no one quite understands exactly what their particular family is struggling with.

Some further thoughts about families come from meeting and listening to many in the course of my work. My observations are borne out by the research referred to above.

The impact on siblings

I have written elsewhere about the impact on siblings of a child with developmental delay or special needs (Bartram, 2007). The brothers and sisters of children with developmental difficulties have an increased vulnerability to psychological problems. They may worry that they are less loved than their sibling because of the amount of time and mental energy parents have to put into their care. However, it may be hard to express this, for fear of adding to the parents' worries. Some children respond to having a sibling with developmental delay by identifying with the caring role and feeling too responsible for their well-being. This can sometimes arise from feeling guilty that, unlike their sibling, they do not have any developmental problems.

Siblings can also sometimes feel that they have to grow up quickly and minimise their own needs for time and attention, to ensure that their developmentally delayed sibling gets what he needs. This can lead to long-term psychological problems in the well-developing sibling. Anger and resentment can "go underground" and re-emerge later in life in the context of new relationships.

Tina, Kieran's foster carer, is able to provide an environment where the children she cares for can voice their complaints about how sometimes one child is treated differently from another. 'We

31

treat the children equally but not the same. If one complains that Kieran is allowed something he can't have, I remind him that he can go alone to the shops, and Kieran is not allowed to do that.' Tina is not hampered by guilt, it seems, when it comes to treating the children in her care differently from, but equally to, each other.

The impact on parental relationships

It is not uncommon to find that a response to the challenges of raising a child with developmental delay can include a polarisation in a partnership, both practically and emotionally. If only one partner has a job, he or she may throw themselves into work, leaving the other partner to manage the diary of appointments and to attend them with the child alone. The divorce and separation rate for parents of children with special needs may be understood both in terms of meeting the practical demands of earning, getting enough sleep and seeing that children's needs are met, as well as the emotional demands of dealing with sadness and other feelings.

The impact on single parents

Single adopters and foster carers have the advantage of being able to concentrate on their child with special needs without having to consider a partner. However, lone parents bear all the practical, financial and emotional responsibility and also need support from others. It is important that all parents attend to their own emotional needs: find time for themselves, risk having a babysitter, no matter how dangerous that can sometimes feel, and enjoy time and relationships outside the home.

The impact on extended family

It can be easy to forget that members of the extended family are also affected by having a child in the family who has additional needs. Parents sometimes report that their own parents don't believe the child has any real difficulties, but that their "bad behaviour" is a result of how they are being brought up. It can be helpful for extended family members to be included in medical and therapy appointments, so they can develop a shared understanding of what is happening and can both offer and receive support.

Containment

"Containment" is a term used by some practitioners for a particular psychological function, which parents and carers fulfil for their child when all goes well (Bion, 1967, p. 140). It is an idea of central importance in some schools of psychology, in particular psychoanalytic thinking. The concept of containment expresses the idea that in the course of any child's life there are experiences such as hunger, fear or loneliness which cause anxiety and distress for the child. When a baby feels that distress, he communicates it, without the use of words, to his parents or carers. He does this by, as it were, "infecting" the parent figure with his own feelings. So, for example, a baby who is hungry or in pain expresses it in such a way that it is felt by the parent. If the baby's distress then sends the parent into great distress, the situation can potentially spiral: the parent's distress "re-infects" the baby, and so escalates his own initial distress. In contrast to this, when the parent can receive the baby's communication of distress and "contain" it, that is to say, hold on to it and digest it rather than re-transmit it, then the baby's distress can be held within the carer, and the baby is relieved of it.

Children who have developmental difficulties have more challenges than other children in terms of what they bring into the world. The baby who requires repeated surgery and injections, who spends months of his life in hospital, has more challenges to his sense of well-being than an ordinarily developing baby. He may cry more than another baby, or perhaps be quieter and less responsive than he might otherwise have been. Similarly, children who cannot express themselves through language or make sense of the world because of cognitive limitations, or who cannot explore the world physically through touch and movement, may have very high needs for containment.

Thus we can see that parents or carers, as well as their children, have more to manage than might have been predicted. They will have to manage their own feelings, which may be of helplessness or despair or anger, in the face of the child's developmental difficulties. However, to the extent that they are able to do this, they will be able to offer the baby or child the containment they need for their emotional and psychological well-being.

One of the biggest problems experienced by the birth parents of children with developmental difficulties is the feeling of guilt. Guilt can get in the way of offering emotional containment, because it takes up so much of the parents' psychological energy. Parents who foster or adopt children with developmental difficulties are much less prone to this disabling guilt. This can free them to offer containment in terms of receiving children's communications and also, unlike James' mother above, they may feel free to set boundaries, perhaps precisely because they do not blame themselves for the difficulties in their child's development.

CHAPTER 5

What the children say: findings from child psychotherapy

Child psychotherapy is a way of working with children troubled by emotional problems, which may manifest themselves in different ways. Child psychotherapy is largely a non-directive method: one aim is to help children to express, verbally or through play, their thoughts and feelings, many of which they are, at least initially, unaware of. Child psychotherapy is predicated on the idea that the therapist offers containment for the child, in a way which resembles the containment offered by the ordinary "good enough" parent or carer (see Chapter 4). It may be offered when ordinary "good enough" methods of caring are not sufficient to contain whatever the child is troubled by. At such times, behaviour and feelings may break through or "burst out", expressing themselves in symptoms, for example, aggressive behaviour, depression, anxiety or relationship difficulties.

Child psychotherapists work with a wide range of children and this includes children and young people who have developmental delay. Because the method does not depend on the child being verbally articulate, it is a very useful way of getting to know and coming to an understanding of children who have difficulty expressing themselves in words.

Not all children who have developmental delay will need specialist psychological help. However, in this chapter I will introduce some children with developmental delay who did have child psychotherapy, in order to show their preoccupations, what they managed to convey to the therapist about themselves and to consider how this gives us an insight into their experience of themselves, their key relationships and their emotional lives.

When a child is adopted or fostered this is always a new beginning, which brings with it hope. However, as we saw when thinking about the whole child in Chapter 3, the factors that interact within a child begin to come into play from the very start of life. Whatever a child feels about himself or herself is already in the making at the time of adoption or fostering.

Therefore, below I introduce Louise and Joshua, to illustrate their inner worlds as well as how change was possible for them, and how this affected their quality of life and relationships with others.

Louise

Louise had no formal diagnosis of developmental delay, but her progress at school was limited and her concentration poor. Her school had requested an assessment for a statement of special educational needs, so she could have extra help and support. She was referred for child psychotherapy at the age of eight by her school SENCO (Special Educational Needs Co-ordinator), because of her physical and verbal aggression towards her adoptive mother and older brother. She was described as having violent and furious rages when she was not allowed to have her own way and there had been some incidents of self-harm, which were felt to be extreme for a child of her age. She was excessively jealous of her brother, had poor peer relationships, suffered from nightmares and had separation anxiety, especially when going from home to school.

Louise had an unstable family background and disturbed relationships from birth until she was adopted, aged three. By the time she came to the clinic, her adoptive mother felt neither well nor strong enough to manage Louise without professional help. Her mother's focus at the start of treatment was Louise's anger; this was what she felt she needed most help with.

Louise initially presented as chatty and smiley, but her psychotherapist had a feeling that this might be a way of covering up and distracting both the psychotherapist and herself from her more troubled feelings. Her therapist also noted that she did not explore the room or the toys offered and this inhibition of curiosity seemed to belie her apparent confidence.

As time went on and Louise began to show more of herself, her therapist was very struck by the "toddlerish" nature of her play, which was at odds with her chronological age. She liked to play messily with the tea set and the playdough, often creating floods and mess in the room. Louise seemed to convey an experience of herself as overflowing and flooded, perhaps full of feelings which were too much for her to hold inside herself. The therapist noticed that she herself often felt angry about the mess created by Louise in the room. She began to wonder whether all this messiness was expressing something about Louise's angry feelings through play, without words.

Louise was also very bossy and controlling, often reversing roles so that the therapist felt small, helpless and out of control, while

37

Louise seemed to take charge. Again, this appeared to be a communication of Louise's own feelings, which she seemed to be asking her psychotherapist to feel on her behalf.

In terms of Louise's stage of development, she seemed stuck in the pre-latency stage and this was creating many problems for her relationships and learning.

As Louise's sessions continued, an important theme emerged of deprivation. She conveyed that she felt there was never enough of anything. Her therapist talked to her about how this made her anxious but also angry. Sometimes Louise mocked her therapist and accused her of not being able to do something correctly. This seemed linked with her own difficulties at school where she could not enjoy academic success. Gradually, it became possible to talk about her low opinion of her own abilities and how upsetting this was for her.

Over two years of psychotherapy, Louise changed considerably as these themes were contained and worked through in her relationship with her psychotherapist. There were improvements in all aspects of her behaviour, including her capacity to concentrate and to learn. Her mother reported a much improved relationship with her daughter. By the end of therapy, Louise had given up her messy play and was predominantly functioning in a way typical of latency children, using the dolls and the dolls' house to play out scenes and relationships between children and adults; she was more able to talk and express herself verbally rather than through behaviour.

It seemed that Louise's overriding experience at the start of therapy was feeling out of control, and of low value. Instead of being able to tell her mother how she felt, she had been showing her by acting out in many different ways. Psychotherapy helped Louise to move from this position to a place where her emotions were understood, less chaotic and more ordered inside her. Consequently, her capacity to think straight and to express herself developed, and this was manifested in all aspects of her life. I am not suggesting, of course, that psychotherapy cured Louise's learning difficulties. In fact, her therapist was instrumental in supporting the process started by the school of getting extra educational help for her, in recognition of her learning disability. Her psychotherapy, however, was able to address her experience as a child who struggled with both constitutional and environmental challenges; it enabled her to take a developmental step from a predominantly toddlerish state of mind, to one more conducive to co-operation and formal learning.

Joshua

Joshua was fostered at the age of five when his mother was no longer able to care for him because of her mental illness. He sustained a brain injury during the birth process and has cerebral palsy. The events around his birth were traumatising for his birth parents and they separated when he was just a few months old, leaving a fragile mother to care for him alone. Joshua was delayed in meeting all his milestones, although psychological testing at the age of 10 showed that his intelligence was within the normal range. Joshua looked physically different from his peers, and struggled to use the right side of his body and his right arm and leg; his speech could be hard to understand.

At the age of 11, he was at the point of entering puberty, a stage of development when children become increasingly self-conscious and aware of differences between themselves and others. His paediatrician felt that this might be a good time for him to have some additional support from a psychotherapist, to help him to negotiate this developmental step.

SECTION I

Two main themes emerged in Joshua's psychotherapy: the first was of an almost constant experience of having been set an impossibly difficult task and the hard work involved in tackling it; the second was of being trapped. In both cases, Joshua communicated these preoccupations not by talking about them, as would an adult, but by putting his therapist in the position of the person who had these experiences, first-hand.

Joshua introduced make-believe games in which his therapist always had to work very hard, was accused of being slow and lazy or of not trying hard enough to achieve. The therapist often felt exhausted by the constant demands on her and convinced that whatever she did would never be either enough or "the right thing". The therapist reflected on this experience and talked to Joshua about how he wanted her to understand what it feels like for everything to be a struggle. This was most noticeable when he was trying to stick things together with glue or tape, and what was meant to be a constructive activity became messy, entangled and hopelessly counterproductive

Joshua also conveyed his sense of being trapped, which perhaps related to his lively and intelligent mind, whose expression was severely hampered by his body and speech: he tied up the therapist's arms and legs and put her "in a dungeon" from which she could not escape. Joshua would say with great feeling, 'Your mummy and daddy are dead and you are all alone in the dungeon!' The therapist was given a very personal experience of feeling alone and in despair.

As Joshua's therapy progressed, the twin themes of impossibly hard work, and being trapped, developed and changed. The dungeon game was replaced by other games in which he expressed a sense of himself as freer and more empowered. Although his physical body had not changed, his sense of himself changed. His therapist was also allowed to be freer in the sessions.

In his peer relationships, Joshua became more assertive. These changes seemed to set him up for the challenges with which he would undoubtedly be faced in adolescence.

I hope that these voices of two children in psychotherapy show not only their preoccupations, but also the way in which they communicated by putting or "projecting" into the therapist their own unwanted and difficult experiences. When the therapist was able to bear and to understand this as a communication, the children became able to develop and change.

Carers of children with developmental delay may well receive disturbing communications at times in the form of action or behaviour. They too may be made to feel that they are disabled in their capacity to parent a child with developmental delay, or that they are full of chaotic and messy feelings, or unable to think straight. It is worth remembering that far from this being the case, these may be communications from the child about how he or she feels about himself or herself. When the child can be helped with these bad feelings, through understanding, containment and thoughtful firmness, both child and carer may feel freer to enjoy living well together.

SECTION I

41

CHAPTER **6**

Life today, life tomorrow

It is probably clear from the children and young people described so far that developmental delay often brings with it some disturbance of ordinary daily living. This might be expressed in unusual sleeping or eating, or in unusual and sometimes troublesome behaviour. As we have heard from the voices of children in psychotherapy, children and young people with developmental delay can be troubled by difficult feelings of being different, restricted, carrying a burden or struggling to feel at home within themselves and in the world around them.

Families vary very much in terms of how far these disturbances of daily living cause them distress and lead them to seek professional help outside the family. What one family can live with, another finds challenging, and yet another intolerable. One family adapts to a child's differences, while another may feel stretched beyond their maximum flexibility.

For birth parents, as I have already indicated, guilt can complicate the task of parenting immeasurably. The absence of guilt, however, is a great starting point for adopting or fostering a child or young person with developmental delay.

I was very struck by the accounts given to me by Tina and Sally, a foster carer and adoptive parent respectively, of daily life with the children they care for. Tina described Kieran when he came to live with her: he was scratching, rocking and hitting, could not be left without adult supervision, had a short attention span, a lack of awareness of others' personal space and oppositional behaviour, which used to include refusing to wear a seat belt in the car. He also had an anxiety about food, always worrying that there wouldn't be enough. Some of these characteristics had improved dramatically over the years spent with her family; others had stayed almost the same.

Sally told me, with equanimity, that her adoptive son, Ethan, was at about a two- to three-year level when he came to live with them, aged four; now, 10 years later, she would say he is 'still the same'. He still likes the same toys he did then, musical toys and pop-up toys. Ethan has not developed speech although his understanding has improved. He has always responded badly to change, and still does. He paces and claps, and from the start had challenging behaviour and was very anxious if leaving the house. He needs one-to-one supervision. He likes to run taps, would open knife drawers and he has broken a television set. Like Kieran, he has made some progress in some areas, but in others, he is 'just himself'. Sally told me it doesn't 'faze' them. 'That's life with Ethan, and your life does change.'

To my surprise, in neither case do these disturbances of daily life dominate Sally's or Tina's account of caring for a delayed young person. They are facts to be taken into consideration, but by no means the most important thing they wanted to tell me about

SECTION I

life with their children. Tina stressed to me the personal value of feeling that she had made a big difference to Kieran's life, and Sally, birth mother of two daughters, described Ethan as 'the son we never had'. Sally also described how fighting for Ethan's place in society had made her a stronger and more confident person than she would have been without him.

It seems clear that while a good home can make a great deal of difference to the well-being of children and young people with developmental delay, part of the skill of the carer is to be able to accept what cannot change and accept the child as a whole person; at the same time, the carer must offer emotional containment and robust responses when the child presents the family and the wider world with difficulties which can and ought to be tackled. The knack, of course, is in being able to tell one situation from the other, in an ever-changing and evolving family environment.

Earlier, I considered the strain that testing and appointments can place on a family, but of course it is also true that invaluable support and help can be forthcoming from professionals in schools, health, social care and the voluntary sector. When the right sort of help in the right quantity can be accessed, parents and professionals can work in a partnership that is truly creative.

Transitions and looking to the future

In recent years, health and social care policy has turned its attention, with good reason, to the issue of transition from children's services to adult services. Resources for adults with disabilities and developmental difficulties vary greatly from area to area. Kieran's foster carer hopes that when he is a young adult, he may be able to access "supported living" where he could live relatively independently, but with support on hand from professional carers. In other geographical areas, this option is not a possibility and adults go on living with their families for as long as their parents or carers are alive.

However, all transitions, and not only the transition into adulthood, are emotionally challenging and disturbing to some extent, even when the transition is chosen rather than enforced, and felt to be for the better rather than the worse. A parent or carer may be pleased when their young child starts school but also aware that now their child's day will include many experiences from which they are excluded. If the child has very limited communication skills, then they will not be able to say what they have done or what has happened and this can make the process of separation and letting go more difficult. Whatever the gain, transitions are a time of loss and change.

When, like Aaron in Chapter 3, a docile child transitions into the stormy waters of adolescence, the sense of loss for the parent or carer can be profound. As adulthood approaches, parents of a developmentally delayed young person have to confront dilemmas about separation and independence, which all parents have to face, but writ large. Ultimately there is always the question as to who will care for the young person, and how well, when the parents or carers are dead or no longer able to care. As young people move into adulthood, parents and carers have to contemplate their own deaths and a future when they will no longer be around to look after the vulnerable adult their child will become. This may confront parents and carers with great anxiety which, if it can be faced, will hopefully lead to constructive planning.

Conclusion

I hope I have given an idea of the range of children and young people described as having developmental delay, the challenges families face in terms of assessment and diagnosis and the value of thinking about the whole child rather than only about a label or diagnosis. I have also referred to what helps families to meet those challenges and enjoy the rewards of living with a developmentally delayed child.

Undoubtedly, foster carers and adopters are freer from the burden of guilt which birth parents often carry in relation to having made a baby with developmental problems. Perhaps this insight opens up a way of thinking about how the strengths and qualities of non-birth parents and carers can help us as individuals and as a society, to understand more about how life can be lived well with children and young people with developmental delay.

References

Bartram P (2007) *Understanding Your Young Child with Special Needs*, Tavistock series, London: Jessica Kingsley Publishers

Bartram P (2009) 'The eye of the sea: a response to the article, "TAC for the 21st century: a unifying theory about children who have multifaceted disabilities"', in Limbrick P (ed) *Interconnexions*, 7, available at: www.teamaroundthechild.com/issue/issue-number-7. html

Bion W (1967) *Second Thoughts*, London: Maresfield Library

Emerson E and Hatton C (2007) *The Mental Health of Children and Adolescents with Learning Disabilities in Britain*, Lancaster: Institute for Health Research, Lancaster University

Jacobs B and Miles L (2012) *Parenting a Child with Attention Deficit Hyperactivity Disorder*, London: BAAF

Marks D (1999) *Disability: Controversial Debates and Psychosocial Perspectives*, London: Routledge

Matson JL and Marchetti A (eds) (1988) *Developmental Disabilities: A life-span perspective*, Philadelphia: Grune and Stratton

McInley I and Holland J (1986) 'Mentally handicapped children' in Gordon G and McInley I (eds) *Neurologically Handicapped Children: Treatment and management*, London: Blackwell

Polnay L and Hull D (1985) *Community Paediatrics*, London: Churchill Livingstone

Salt A and Gringas P (2004) 'Developmental delay', in Moyer VA, Elliot EJ and Davis RL (eds) *Evidence Based Paediatrics and Child Health*, London: BMJ

SECTION 1

PARENTING CHILDREN AFFECTED BY DEVELOPMENTAL DELAY

SUE AND JIM CLIFFORD

How our
family grew

Our family is not as we planned it. What family is...
but our plans changed beyond recognition. When we
married, we discussed what size our family would be
and decided we wanted a large one. Large to us then
was four children: two birth children and two adopted
children. Birth children did not happen so we went for
Plan B, and decided that all four of our children would
be adopted.

We started small and had two sisters placed with us
in 1990, who were then aged six and nine. They were
formally adopted two years later, and in 1994 we
completed our planned family when two brothers, aged
seven and eight, were placed with us.

However, 10 years on our family was almost grown

up and four children didn't seem enough. So in 2004 a sibling group of four children – two sisters and two brothers – joined our family, and in 2008 another little girl was placed with us. With nine children, we do now have a large family, which may finally be complete.

In the 1990s, attachment disorder, developmental trauma disorder, therapeutic parenting and, indeed, adoption support, were barely a glimmer on the horizon. We had read the earlier work of John Bowlby and others and, although we didn't fully understand it at the time, we had picked up a number of the elements of the therapeutic parenting models, which we now follow to address many of our children's difficulties. Developmental delay in children back then was understood as being "a little bit behind" due to a few missed experiences, and if the child was placed in a loving home they would soon catch up. As you will see, and as we discovered, this is not quite how it works.

Hurdles and progress

Our eldest daughter, Lisa, was certainly educationally delayed and emotionally very insecure, and had difficulty with attachments. She struggled through her teen years to accept us as parents and saw us more as the providers of her material needs. She also struggled at school with reading, maths and organisational skills, which we thought were simply signs of developmental delay due to her many moves in her early years. It wasn't until she was at college, at the age of 17, that she was diagnosed with dyslexia. At the age of 31, she is married with four children and is managing reasonably well. She does now have a strong attachment to us as a family, although she is still insecure and has poor self-esteem.

Our eldest son, Chris, seemed to be managing well and we didn't realise until he was at college that he was developmentally delayed in an emotional sense. He was very "shut down" and dissociated as a result of his early life experiences, and was simply going through the motions of living without any real attachments in life. He expressed no emotion; he did not appear to feel heat, cold, pain, hunger or thirst; he had no real connection to anyone or anything. This meant that he was an easy child to parent as he was growing up, but he was not equipped to manage as an adult as he had developed none of the planning, organising and problem-solving skills. Thankfully, when we realised this in 2003/04, research into attachment difficulties and the effects of early life trauma was being published. With some intensive life story work and therapeutic interventions, we have substantially enabled Chris to catch up emotionally. He is now a well-functioning adult with a job, a car, a girlfriend and a number of interests and hobbies.

Developmental delay in the family, school and community

All of our children came to us developmentally delayed in one or more aspects of their lives, but the one who was most delayed and whose story we now tell is Wayne, our second eldest son (and our fourth eldest child). Wayne had spent three years with his birth mother and four years in foster care before he was placed with us. At the age of seven, he could not run or catch a ball, he could not feed himself, he had only about 100 words and could not form sentences. He was still in nappies. He was happy-go-lucky but with an attention span of about 10 seconds. In our naivety we thought, and indeed the paperwork we received indicated, that given a stable home life and consistent care, Wayne would probably eventually catch up with his peers.

SECTION II

While in his foster home, Wayne had been held back to repeat Year 1 at school. When he moved to our family, he was due to attend a small village school with mixed age classes. The educational psychologist's report, prepared just prior to his move, stated that this would be an ideal setting for him, that it might be possible for him to rejoin his own year group and that, indeed, he had the underlying ability to be able to do so. We held out hope for a bright future for Wayne, and we had the drive to make it happen. We believed that although Wayne was a seven-year-old who was in most ways developmentally like a two-year-old, he would, eventually, catch up.

Wayne was exhausting to parent due to his level of hyperactivity and his poor attention span. His sister, Lisa, on meeting him, asked, 'The little one – what's he on?' He could not really follow even simple instructions, and we often had to stop him, turn him towards us and kneel down to his level to ensure that we had his attention before we could talk to him. Even when he repeated an instruction back to us, he was frequently unable to follow a request – either he didn't understand it or couldn't keep it in mind long enough to comply. One day, Chris and Wayne wanted to help Jim take the engine out of one of our cars. Having released the engine mounts, and with the engine on a hoist and gantry, Jim reached for the screwdriver. It was gone. Chris couldn't find it, so they asked Wayne where it was. 'I put...' he replied. 'Where...?' 'I put....' he insisted. After countless repetitions, they put the engine down and took the garage apart to find the screwdriver carefully secreted in a wall panel.

We concentrated initially on improving Wayne's gross and fine motor skills. Many hours were spent in the park

SECTION II

teaching him to run and throwing a rugby ball to him so
that he could learn how to catch. Mealtimes were also
a struggle as he found it hard to sit at a table and eat
a meal using a knife and fork. His poor attention span
meant that he couldn't sit still for long without fiddling
with everything around him. During introductions, we had
taken the two boys to a seafront fish and chip shop for
lunch. We had expected that, at seven and eight years old,
they would manage the five-minute wait while their food
was brought to the table. However, in order to contain
Wayne, we had to sit at a small table tucked under the
stairs, and we spent the whole mealtime trying to stop
him from climbing onto the table and pouring vinegar
into the salt and pepper pots – a taste of things to come.

Wayne at school

At school, Wayne had a statement of special educational
needs which initially gave him 12 hours of support per
week. The school he attended was a small first school
covering Reception to Year 3. Every day was a challenge
to get him ready for school, and every day when we
collected him we heard from teachers and other
children how "naughty" he had been. He couldn't sit
down in assembly and was often withdrawn from class
due to his hyperactivity, which disrupted everyone else's
learning. He was friendly towards everyone, although not
always appropriate in his interactions with adults. He was
popular with his peers but they were also a little scared
of him; he was often not invited to friends' parties and
was on the outside of social circles. He learned to play
games, he could eat his school lunch independently and
was no longer in nappies during the day. However, he
was still bed-wetting and struggling to manage social
interactions.

SECTION II

55

Wayne had no understanding of ownership and helped himself to others' belongings, although he was happy to hand them back when asked. So every day he came home from school with a pocketful of rubbers, which he had collected from the pots of stationery on each table, and next morning he returned them with an apology. We hoped that eventually he would learn not to take what didn't belong to him, but he never did, and as he became older he took other things such as games trading cards, keys, mobile phones and money. He knew what stealing was, and that stealing was wrong, but he could not make the connection between stealing and what he was doing. His logic for this behaviour was that the items were not on someone's person, so they didn't belong to anyone. Nothing valuable could be left lying around – everything had to be locked away.

The distorted logic Wayne applied to stealing was also applied to pretty much every area of his life. One day, at his first school, someone kicked a football over the fence. Wayne wanted to help get it back so, unbeknown to us, he "borrowed" his dad's lock-knife which, when opened, was just long enough to reach under the fence and knock the football close enough to reach. Of course, there was the immediate phone call home to ask why our son had such a dangerous weapon in school.

"Wayne logic", as we called it, came into play constantly as he failed, and continues to fail, in understanding social cues and expectations. A visit to watch Premiership rugby saw a player kick the ball over the stand in which we were sitting. Wayne leapt out of his seat, ready to run down the stairs towards the exit. He was worried that someone would steal the ball and ruin the game.

Throughout his three years in first school, we struggled to help Wayne to catch up academically, and worked hard on his motor skills and social skills. At home, his hyperactivity meant that he was everywhere all the time and we had to watch him constantly. He was fascinated with exploring his environment like a two-year-old. He had no awareness of danger and was always doing dangerous things like playing with sharp knives and matches. He managed to set fire to the trees in the garden and cut though the 240-volt electric armoured cables which operate the pump to the garden fountain. The minute we took our eyes off him, he was putting himself and others at risk.

Like his brother, Wayne didn't have the physical sensations of heat and cold, hunger and thirst and pain. It was not long before he was dry and clean during the day, but it was seven years before he was dry at night. Despite trying every possible strategy, nothing worked. We were referred to the enuresis clinic and given the usual alarms and mats to go on the bed, and then treated as stupid when we said they didn't work. It was a chance encounter with another parent that led us to try a nasal spray, prescribed by the GP, which finally gave us respite from having to change his bed two or three times a night. Our hopes were still there, but it felt harder to keep them up, and they were tempered with a growing feeling that this was not going to be plain sailing.

Not only were school and home a challenge and exhausting, but having any sort of family social life was also very difficult to manage. Wherever we went, Wayne would indiscriminately collect other people's belongings and attach himself to complete strangers, as if he had known them forever. Many friends and acquaintances

SECTION II

57

found his behaviour off-putting and we found ourselves being hyper-vigilant and unable to relax. We could not even talk to friends, as we always had one eye on where Wayne was and what he was up to. Throughout this time, we were also trying to meet the needs of our other three children, of whom the eldest was then already a challenging teenager. The amount of time we spent supervising Wayne did dilute the time we had available for our other children, but on the positive side it also meant that having an additional focus ensured that we were not overwhelmed by the challenging behaviour of our teenage daughter.

The move to adopt the two boys had been a joint family decision, and it had a uniting effect on our daughters' relationship with us and with each other. When first placed in our family, the girls had a combative sibling relationship, but they united in helping their younger brothers to settle into the family. They have always been fiercely protective of them, and their sense of self-worth increased as the boys looked up to them and took their lead from them.

We were fortunate that, just as Wayne went into Year 3, and we were searching for an appropriate middle school for him, his small village school became a full primary school. This gave him another three years in a class of 12 children.

It was still our optimistic belief that over time Wayne would catch up with his peers. We had high expectations and encouraged him to develop and learn to a level which, we now realise, was not possible for him to attain. We and the school taught him to read, and he seemed to be making progress. He could read words and sentences

– but he could not make any sense of what he read. The words were, for Wayne, just words in isolation. He could understand each word in its literal sense, but could not understand the overall content.

His speech was similarly very literal. Over time he learnt, by copying from us and other adults, how to respond in a social situation. Provided that the conversation was of a very general nature, he was able to join in and give the impression that he was functioning at an age-appropriate level. In this sense, we taught him to over-perform, which helped others to be more accepting of him but also masked his difficulties and made it harder, as he became an adult, to access the support he needed.

By the time he was in Year 6 (although a year older than the others in the class), Wayne had made little further progress at school. He was still indiscriminate with strangers, still hyper-active and disruptive in class, still several years behind academically, still unable to understand that by taking others' belongings he was stealing, and still unable to comprehend the context of language. We applied to a secondary school for children with moderate learning difficulties in a neighbouring county, as we believed that this would best suit his needs. However, our local education authority sent a copy of his original statement with our application, instead of his revised statement, and we were turned down because it looked like his needs were too great for them to manage.

We finally managed to get him a place in Year 8 in a middle school in a neighbouring borough. This was a small church school with a good reputation for managing children with special needs. We jumped him from Year

6 to Year 8 as Year 7 was over-subscribed, as this was the only way to secure a place for him. His statement of special educational needs now specified up to 18 hours a week of teaching assistant support, and on the whole he managed this school reasonably well with only a few additional problems.

We, as a family, still had no help at home and adoption support was still something in the future. As a couple, we had little time away from our children, although we did aim to have one weekend on our own each year. We would try to get a close friend or relative to move in while we took time off, but this was usually fraught with complications when they tried to manage Wayne in the way in which we did. They found his behaviours impossible.

Having managed a year in middle school, Wayne now had to move again to upper school. However, just as we applied to the most appropriate upper school in our area, it closed. We had just two weeks to find an alternative. With some frantic phone calls, some hastily arranged meetings, and no help from the local authority, a place was found in a good nurturing secondary school for his final three years of education.

Until this point, we had both been working as accountants, with Jim a partner in a large firm and Sue running her own practice from home and flexing her work around the needs of the children. However, as Wayne's school was now 15 miles from home, and his behaviour was becoming ever more challenging, Sue needed to be close by so she could get to school quickly if there was a problem. She reduced the number of her clients and at the same time took a job working

with special needs students at the college of further
education close to Wayne's new school.

Wayne at secondary school

Wayne was popular in his new school and had
several friends. However, they were ready to take
advantage of his generous nature and his vulnerability
and suggestibility. He still interpreted everything
literally, using his distinct logic. His sunny personality
was endearing to the staff, although they became
frustrated with his limitations, which he demonstrated
by occasional defiance and aggressive or obsessive
behaviour. He continued to steal and lie. His sensory
shut-down was a risk for the school, because when he
hurt himself in science, technology or sport, he did not
realise that he was injured. He was aware that he didn't
feel pain, so would deliberately do dangerous things such
as touching hot pans in food technology lessons to show
off this "skill".

It had been a condition of the school accepting him as a
pupil that Wayne's statement of special educational needs
included 24 hours a week of teaching assistant support.
As a family, we celebrated his progress. However, we
still did not know about attachment disorders and did
not really understand Wayne's behaviours. We were
becoming more and more frustrated with his inability to
conform, and totally exhausted with the effort of trying
to keep him out of trouble and unravel each mess in
which he found himself.

One day, he stole a pot of paint from the art department
at school. One of his friends had told him that he
wanted to paint his bedroom orange but didn't have any
paint. Wayne's logic decreed that this was no problem as

the art department had plenty of orange paint. So during break-time, he just went and helped himself. He then somehow managed to spill some on the stairs and was in trouble both for stealing and for damaging property. The school did not understand "Wayne logic".

On another occasion, two of the girls who were his friends had left their trainers in the girls' PE changing rooms. They needed them at lunchtime so that they could play football, but the changing rooms were kept locked during the lunch hour. To Wayne, this was no problem. He knew that the door of the changing rooms had a metal panel at the bottom, and if he removed it, he could slide through and get their trainers for them. He was caught breaking into the girls' changing rooms and was in trouble again.

Lunchtimes were also a problem. The school operated a canteen system, which required Wayne to bring in money for his lunch. On most days, as a result of his poor concentration and lack of understanding about ownership, he either lost the money or gave it away to a friend. He was excessively generous and could not understand that if he gave his money away then he would not be able to buy lunch. We solved this by giving him a packed lunch, but we had to give him twice as much food as he could eat each day because his friends would often help themselves to some of it. Wayne always wanted to please people and, with no sensation of hunger, he did not even have this as a reminder of his own need for food.

On several occasions, he was in trouble for being defiant and answering teachers back. One day, his teacher had to leave the room for a few minutes and asked the class to keep the door open so that he could hear if the pupils became too noisy. However, Wayne immediately shut the door. When the teacher asked Wayne why he had closed the door, Wayne insisted that doors should always be kept shut. Eventually, we realised what this was about. A part of our house has no heating (we live in a 17th century inn), and we always insist that the door between the unheated part and the rest of the house is kept shut. Wayne's very literal understanding of language meant that he felt that doors always had to be shut because that was what he had learnt at home. The teacher, of course, didn't know this, and believed that Wayne was just being difficult.

Another example of the difficulties caused by Wayne's very literal approach to language was the day when one of the girls at school claimed that she was pregnant and that Wayne was the father. When asked by a teacher if this girl was pregnant and if he was the father, his response was 'maybe'. This resulted in another phone call home and another puzzle for us to solve. What we realised was that Wayne could only deal with one question at a time. Once we separated the two parts of the question, we found that he thought that maybe she was pregnant, but that if she was, he definitely wasn't the father. As it turned out, she wasn't pregnant anyway.

During his years at secondary school, another worrying behaviour started to emerge. Up until then, Wayne had appeared very compliant, and had at least tried to do what he was told. Now, however, we started to see anger and rage when he was feeling frustrated, afraid or misunderstood. On one occasion, some of the children at school were laughing near Wayne and he thought they were laughing at him. Wayne was eating an apple at the time and he got so angry that he threw it. He knew not to throw it at the other children, so he threw it in the opposite direction, straight through a window, and was again in trouble for damaging school property.

Our hope for Wayne was still alive, but taking a battering. It was difficult to see a future for him beyond the "hand-to-mouth" realities of dealing with the daily doses of Wayne-inspired chaos. On many occasions, we found items that did not belong to him in his school bag, and were given some quite fantastic explanations as to how he had acquired them. In order to monitor what was happening in school, particularly with his friends, and to gain an understanding about how he acquired these items, we took to giving several of his friends lifts home in our 12-seater Land Rover. By listening to the conversations between Wayne and his friends, we were able to unravel many of his bizarre activities and alert staff before things got out of hand.

Wayne's communication skills appeared to be improving as he learned more appropriate responses, and he was able to fit in a little better on social occasions. We had always known that he struggled to process language in the way that we did, but thought this was simply a developmental delay that would improve over time. However, by the end of Year 9 he was assessed as having a specific language disorder. This wasn't developmental delay – it was a recognised disability. The school had a specialist resource for children of average ability with a language disorder, and Wayne was assessed as being right on the border of average ability and with a definite language disorder. This seemed to confirm what we had been told when he was first placed with us – that he would eventually catch up with his peers. He had the ability to achieve, it was just his language disorder that was getting in the way. With extra help from speech and language therapists, he would be "sorted".

In order for Wayne to take up the place available in the language unit, the wording on his statement had to be changed from "moderate learning difficulty" to "average ability with a language disorder". We were told this on the day after school ended in July and we had until the first day back at school in September to have his statement changed – just six weeks. We didn't want our application to get lost in the system so we put together our own comprehensive report and worded it in such a way that no extra work was needed; our report could be presented to the panel as if it had been written by the statementing officer. We delivered our report by hand to the education department on 28 August, and requested that the changes be approved before 4 September. Within 48 hours, a team meeting had been held and agreement had been reached in principle to amend the statement as required. The case officer hand-delivered the revised statement to our home.

For his final two years in secondary school, Wayne was in a class of six pupils in the I-CAN speech and language unit. He accessed lessons in the mainstream school but always with support, and all lessons were followed up with reinforcement lessons back in the base unit. During this time, Sue also took a job at the school, working in the speech and language unit, to be available when Wayne displayed challenging behaviours.

By monitoring things so closely, we succeeded in getting Wayne through the whole of his time at secondary school without a single day's exclusion. However, there

SECTION II

were still challenges. It has always been the rule in our family that our children do not have mobile phones until they are 16. Since his 16th birthday, mobile phones have had a particular fascination for Wayne and have also caused him many difficulties. Just a few days after he was given his first phone, he lent it to a friend who said he needed it. His older sister had to go to the friend's house to retrieve the phone for him.

By the time Wayne left school, he had gained passes in certificates of achievement in English, maths and science and even had a GCSE in food technology – not a high grade, but a GCSE nonetheless. We were enormously proud of his success. We still hoped that one day he would catch up and in the meantime we would continue to support him.

Wayne at college

When he was 16, we managed to secure Wayne a place at a mainstream college of further education on a course specifically designed for students with learning difficulties. The course focused on developing life skills, alongside classes in horticulture and animal management. This suited Wayne well as he loved practical activities such as gardening and looking after our two dogs.

Travel to college promised to be easy to manage and we were encouraged by college staff to help him to be as independent as possible. Sue would drive four miles to the local town and drop Wayne at the bus stop where he could catch his college bus. At the end of the day, the staff would put him back on the college bus, and when it arrived at the bus stop where he had caught it in the morning, he would get off and catch the local bus home from the same stop. We had practised numerous times over the summer, taking him into town so that he could catch the bus home. However, on the very first day, the college bus driver didn't stop at the right stop, and even though Wayne saw him drive past the stop, he expected him to return to it. When the bus terminated its journey in the next town, Wayne had a six-mile walk home. He was frustrated and anxious, and when he felt like this he was unable to answer his phone – it became too stressful for him. We were both out for the evening. Luckily, his older sister, who could drive, and his older brother went on a search for him and managed to find him quite quickly on a country road about four miles away, trying to walk home.

This was a taste of things to come. Once he missed the morning bus to college because he had been buying sweets at the kiosk in the bus station. He walked all the way to college, arriving at two in the afternoon. On another day, he left his bag at the kiosk and couldn't remember what he had done with it. After three days the kiosk manager looked in the bag and, because we had written our phone number inside the bag, he rang us and we were able to retrieve it.

Wayne was learning new skills but was unable to transfer them to other situations. He was still easily frustrated and became angry and aggressive when things didn't go as expected. He was fascinated by gadgets and helped himself to any left lying about. There was a constant risk that he would be arrested for breaking the law.

On the whole though, things were going well at this stage. Wayne had started college in September 2003, and with all of our children now almost grown up, we felt ready to take on more children. So we began our

67

home study for our next group of four children. We still needed to monitor Wayne reasonably closely, but continued to be optimistic that he would be able to lead an independent life with minimum support. However, in May 2004 our hopes came crashing down with a bump. We were now approved to take more children and were actively looking for new additions to our family, when we had a phone call from college to say that another student had reported his phone missing, and it was believed that Wayne had taken it.

When Wayne came home we discovered that he had indeed taken the phone, which had been left by its owner, with his bag, at the edge of the pitch while he played football. Wayne had seen it lying there, and had decided that it didn't belong to anyone so he could help himself. The next day the phone – minus its SIM card – was returned to the owner. However, another student was angry with Wayne for what he had done and picked a fight with him. Wayne, now in a rage, and having been taken by a member of staff back to his classroom, proceeded to destroy the classroom. He threw chairs and tables, punched walls and broke the door. We collected him from college and kept him home the next day.

The staff at the college were very understanding. They said that if Wayne promised not to take anyone else's phone and to control his anger, he could return to college. We were asked to promise as well, on his behalf. We knew that Wayne was not able to keep such a promise, and so he was not able to return to college.

Wayne at home full-time

By this time, we had started reading about attachment

disorder and realised that Wayne probably had this, together with foetal alcohol syndrome and possibly other conditions as well as developmental delay, or perhaps as part of his developmental delay. We had no professionals to turn to because at this time there was no adoption support – as far as we knew. This was a very dark period for us. We felt our hope draining away, and couldn't see a future for our much-loved youngest child. We now had a 17-year-old who had learning difficulties and challenging behaviours at home full-time. His developmental delay was no longer something that was a temporary state. It was a lifelong disability which somehow we had to manage.

Sue was now also at home with Wayne full-time. She could no longer go anywhere without him. Even going to the supermarket was a challenge as he would indiscriminately engage strangers in conversation, or butt in when they were talking to friends. He loved small children and would want to play with them, which made him seem threatening to their parents. He also liked to help himself to items from the shelves, which he might then try to sneak into his pockets.

Through Connexions, a careers service for 14–19 year-olds, Sue managed to have Wayne enrolled on an Entry to Employment (E2E) course. This was for two hours a day, and if he attended every day he was paid £40 per week. The course was designed for six weeks, but Wayne remained on it for 15 months, from June 2004 to September 2005. Whilst talking to his Connexions adviser, Sue learnt about Camphill, a charity that runs schools, colleges and adult communities for young people with learning difficulties. The Connexions worker suggested that this might be a way forward for Wayne in

SECTION II

69

the long term. Our hope revived. After much research, we applied to a Camphill college in Gloucestershire in spring 2005. An assessment day was held in September, and as a result Wayne was offered a place for September 2006, subject to funding being agreed through a government body called the Learning Skills Council.

During this time, in July 2004, a sibling group of four children was placed with our family. We were learning about their needs and their developmental delay, while meeting the continuing challenges of parenting Wayne. It was also at this time that Sue went to a conference and learned about the changes in the legislation that entitled us to an assessment of adoption support needs for a child placed a long time ago. We immediately contacted social services and requested an assessment of adoption support needs for Wayne. Thankfully, he was still under 18 and entitled to it. The assessment was completed, and one of the recommendations was a referral to CAMHS. An initial appointment was offered in September 2004, but there was no follow-up until April 2005, and then only after repeated requests. Some kind of talking therapy was started, but Wayne was not able to make any use of it due to his general developmental delay. We spoke to the CAMHS psychiatrist and suggested that instead of therapy, a more productive route might be to assess him and give him a more formal diagnosis in order for all the professionals to have a better understanding of his difficulties and future prognosis. We were fortunate to be working with a psychiatrist who was willing to listen and who realised that in terms of understanding Wayne, we, and not the professionals, were the experts.

Various psychological and psychiatric assessments were

carried out between June 2005 and April 2008 before we had a diagnosis which fully covered his difficulties. On occasions, there were gaps of several months between appointments, and every time we started to make headway, it seemed that we had done such a good job that Wayne's problems were not recognised by professionals. Many times we were in despair, but eventually we succeeded in getting a diagnosis. Wayne is described by the psychiatrist as having 'global impairments in his intellectual, emotional and social functioning'. He has mental impairment, which is defined as 'a state of arrested and incomplete development of mind which includes significant impairment of intelligence and social functioning and is associated with abnormally aggressive or seriously irresponsible conduct'. No longer were we looking at developmental delay in the sense of a gap that Wayne could make up if we had enough hope, belief and energy. Our son now had an enduring condition that is life-long.

In addition to having an assessment of adoption support needs carried out in 2004, when Wayne was 17, we also requested that he be allocated a social worker to help us to access appropriate services for him. We approached the team that supports families of children with learning disabilities, and were told that Wayne was too old for children's services and too young for adult services. There was no help or support until a social worker was finally allocated in December 2005, 18 months after our first request. The list below shows some of the challenging behaviours we were managing by then on a day by day, hour by hour basis.

Wayne's challenging behaviours at home as a young adult

- Theft – money, phones, keys, SIM cards

- Shoplifting

- Carrying knives in public places

- Shouting and swearing

- Kicking and punching doors and walls

- Lying

- No concept of cause and effect

- Setting fires and cutting through electrical cables

- Over-familiarity with strangers, particularly young children

However, Wayne was also our much-loved son: endearing, kind-hearted, generous and eager to please. His brothers and sisters loved him and were very sensitive about his needs. He enjoyed family events and holidays, was kind and caring to his grandma and his great-aunt who were both regular visitors, and was taking an active role at our church as a door steward (with some help).

By September 2005, Wayne had finished his E2E course and was sent by Connexions to another local college of further education to do an additional course to develop independence skills in young people with learning difficulties. We were not overly optimistic, but once again we were encouraged to teach him independent travel. His journey this time involved a bus, a train and a short walk through the town centre past lots of exciting shops. On numerous occasions he was late arriving at college, having been distracted by the shops. On even more

occasions, he was over three hours late returning from college, with no rational explanation; we had no means of contacting him because he would not answer his phone if he was not where he should have been.
Even when he was travelling home as he should, things often went wrong. There was one time when, having paid his fare and boarded the bus at the bus station, he and all the other passengers were asked to get off and board the bus behind, as the bus they were on had broken down. He knew that he had to pay for a ticket if he boarded the bus, and as he had no money left (having just bought a ticket for the bus that had broken down), he walked the four miles home. He did not realise that he could use his ticket on the new bus.

Another example of "Wayne logic" was when he made a cheesecake at college. On that particular day there was a review meeting at the college, which was to be attended by us as his parents, his social worker, his college tutor and him. Everyone arrived and there was no sign of Wayne, despite his having been reminded several times during the day not to go home after college. A friend of his said he'd gone into town. He finally arrived 20 minutes late. He knew his cheesecake needed to be kept in a fridge and was worried about it being unrefrigerated during the meeting, so he had been asking in the electrical appliance shops in town whether one of them would keep it in their fridge, and he would collect it later. Of course, no one would do such a bizarre thing, but to him it had seemed a perfectly logical request.

Having secured the place at the Camphill Residential College for September 2006, we set about putting together the evidence we needed for our funding application to the Learning Skills Council.

73

Because we had taught Wayne to manage basic social communication, which enabled him to appear to fit in to social situations, the new report from adult speech and language services said that he had no real problems, and any shortcomings he did have were due to our not having given him enough life experiences to develop his language skills. We knew this wasn't the case, as we have encouraged him to have as many life experiences as possible. He had been a member of the Boys' Brigade since he became our son, and was enrolled in the Duke of Edinburgh's Award Scheme (in which we were both involved, Jim as an instructor). We had taken him to many different places, including tour group holidays to Switzerland, Peru, Bolivia and Northern Sweden. We had helped him to travel to and from college independently. He was encouraged to join in conversations with his other siblings, one of whom has a degree in English. We had spent countless hours working to improve his understanding of language and he just hadn't developed the skills he needed.

Fortunately, by the time our funding application was ready, we had plenty of other evidence of his difficulties. However, before we could submit the application, we received a letter in January 2006 to say that the Camphill College we had chosen had some internal problems, and could no longer offer Wayne a place for September. Our search started again and it took three months to find an alternative Camphill College with a vacancy, in Wales. Our rollercoaster of despair and hope continued.

Wayne attended a five-day assessment visit before being offered a place, and for the first time, and to our huge relief, we knew we had found somewhere where his difficulties were fully understood. The list below shows the deficits in his life skills which we had recognised and managed but which no one else had seemed to understand. All of these were picked up in the assessment produced by Camphill.

Deficits in Wayne's life skills

- Poor concentration skills

- Unable to choose appropriate clothes for weather

- Unable to focus on tasks for more than three minutes at a time without reminders

- Unable to remember personal hygiene routine without constant reminders

- Easily led by others

- Difficulties making himself understood and easily frustrated if he is not understood

- Can get silly or be in trouble if firm boundaries are not reinforced

- Appears confident when given instructions but in reality often has little idea of what is expected

- Often shows immature behaviour and does not understand normal social cues

We had to work very quickly to secure the funding for September, but we did it. There was now a light at the end of a very long tunnel. Not only did we have a residential place secured for Wayne, but from early 2006 we also finally had some respite ourselves.

Through Wayne's social worker, we were able to apply for direct payments – money paid by social services to enable us to employ a "buddy" for 10 hours a week to take Wayne out for activities, or keep him occupied at home. With his buddy, he was able to go swimming, go for bike rides, go bowling or just go out to lunch. It was not easy to find, and supervise, suitable buddies. They varied from the mature art student who was friendly and communicative and brought his wonderful creative skills to work with Wayne, and the mature trainee mental health nurse (who has since become a family friend), to the part-time health-care worker who was afraid of Wayne and hid from him by washing our clothes and cleaning our house instead of doing activities with him.

Another form of respite was a short break home in our local town, where Wayne could stay for a few nights at a time. The home was purpose-built and could accommodate up to eight people at a time, all with learning difficulties. Carers were on duty 24 hours a day, so he was always well looked after. This was to prove very useful when he came home from college for holidays, as he could share his time between living at home and living in the short break provision. However, this was not without its difficulties. One of the problems for Wayne was an unawareness of the passage of time – he would happily sit up all night playing computer games. We encouraged the staff to set and reinforce sensible bedtimes for him but they argued that, as an adult, he could choose his own bedtime and that it would be an infringement of his human rights to send him to bed at a particular time. Consequently, his health often suffered due to lack of sleep.

Wayne at residential college

When Wayne moved to his residential college in Wales, we continued to explore all possibilities for his long-term future. What was obvious to us was that moving back home full-time after his time away at college was

SECTION 11

not a desirable option. We had been struggling to meet his needs and he had become increasingly frustrated at being less independent than his younger brothers and sisters. The resulting aggression and angry outbursts made life unsafe for everyone. We were concerned for ourselves and for the safety of his four younger siblings. The relief when he went to college was huge and enabled us to take stock and to realise just how exhausted we had become, and how much Wayne's needs were taking us away from meeting the needs of our other children.

Wayne managed three-and-a-half years at the residential college before his behaviours became too extreme for college staff to contain. His time at the college came to an end abruptly. He started to wander the college campus late at night and in the early hours of the morning. He would break into the other houses, steal keys so that he could get into rooms that were out of bounds, enter other students' room while they were sleeping, steal items from their rooms and damage property. The college did not have staff on duty all night, and indeed, when they tried to impose night-time supervision, Wayne became furious and very aggressive.

Wayne's challenging behaviours at residential college

- Acquiring keys

- Acquiring tools from workshops

- Acquiring phones and money belonging to other students and staff

- Manipulative behaviour

- Aggressive outbursts – breaking or throwing objects

- No sense of danger

77

- Running off for several hours when confronted

- Disengaging with tasks when frustrated

- Invasion of the personal space of others

However, Wayne's time at college was generally very positive. The college was run on the Rudolf Steiner principles with a strong bias towards craft, art and music. Students live in houses on the campus, with each house run by house parents, supported by co-workers who provide supervision and encouragement for the students. Daily life is based on a clear routine, which suited Wayne as he needs firm boundaries and structure in order to function well.

Weekdays were a mixture of work and lessons with the focus on developing independence skills. The lessons which suited Wayne best were based on practical skills such as forestry, woodwork, metalwork and cooking. The lessons on relationships and sex education proved more problematic for him. A number of the female students wanted Wayne to be their boyfriend; he always wanted to please everyone, so he agreed and ended up with several girlfriends. This was difficult for Wayne because he felt pressured by so many girls, and it was difficult for the girls because they each wanted to be the only one. Staff helped Wayne to make decisions about what he wanted, but often the girls would not leave him alone. He even ended up having sexual relationships with some of the girls because he did not want to upset them.

As a young man in his early 20s, Wayne has the same desires as any young man of that age, but as he has no impulse control, no sense of cause and effect, and lacks the ability to attach consequences to actions, this area of his life is fraught with difficulties and dangers. He is vulnerable to being accused of sexually abusing others and also vulnerable to being sexually abused himself. Throughout his three-and-a-half years at college, managing this part of his life was a constant problem.

Wayne's time at residential college helped us to gather evidence, in the form of college reports and risk assessments, about the enduring nature of his learning difficulties, his inability to acquire the life skills needed to live independently, and the persistence and escalation of his challenging behaviours. Our son who, 15-and-a-half years previously, we had believed to have developmental delay due to early missed experiences from which he would more or less recover, was now a 23-year-old young man functioning as a five- to six-year-old. He was also displaying behaviours that meant he could no longer live safely in our family home. This was another very dark time for us as a family. What would happen now?

Wayne returned from college for Easter and for good in 2010; we had to stay strong and insist that social services find an alternative placement for him. We knew that if we took him home for even a few days, it would be hard to mobilise them to find him somewhere else to live. So we asked his social worker to meet him from his transport and take him straight to the short break home with which he was already familiar. It felt as though we were abandoning him but we knew that it was right for Wayne and for us. If he had come home he would very quickly have become frustrated with the level of supervision we would have had to impose, and his night wanderings would have put us and our other vulnerable children in danger.

Wayne remained at the respite house for four months whilst a more permanent placement was sought. He now lives in an independent but supported house with five other men, all of whom have learning difficulties and challenging behaviours. There is 24-hour supervision with which Wayne is comfortable because he is living in an environment where everyone has similar care needs. He is able to go to the gym, swimming, cinema and to other leisure activities of his choice. He also has a work experience job as a marshal at a local go-karting centre, which he thoroughly enjoys. He is funded by social services and claims benefits in his own right.

While Wayne was still at college, we talked to him about how he might manage his money when he was living independently from us, and he agreed that he would want our help as he didn't think he could manage it by himself. He was happy to sign Power of Attorney over to us, so we continue to manage his bank account. His benefits go into a savings account and the money he needs on a monthly basis is transferred to a cash account. He has no debit or credit card, just a cash withdrawal card, and any larger items are paid for by us out of his savings.

It has been important for us to ensure that Wayne's life is organised and that he is properly cared for so that if anything should happen to us, his siblings will not be responsible for his care. We believe that we have now achieved that. Our hope and belief-driven rollercoaster seems to have reached the end of the ride.

Living with a child with developmental delay

Living with a child who has developmental delay can be hugely frustrating. You spend hour upon hour trying to teach your child skills for everyday living, only to realise that they may never acquire those skills. It is easy to become frustrated with yourself and your child. It is also very dispiriting when teachers, doctors, therapists and other professionals don't understand your child and his difficulties. If your child is not making the expected progress or is displaying challenging behaviours, the professionals may blame you, as the parents. It is often the case that we can become self-critical and blame ourselves for our child's lack of progress and difficult behaviour. Maybe our parenting is not "good enough".

Sue recalls what many adopters call the "walk of shame" at the end of each day when, on collecting the children from school, she was called into the classroom to listen to the catalogue of misdemeanours our son had committed during the day. Then there were the comments and looks from other parents and children who would come up to her each day as she waited for Wayne, to tell her just how naughty he had been. It is very humiliating if your child is considered to be the naughtiest child in the class, and upsetting to know that really the child is overcoming innumerable challenges, which others seem unable to see.

Managing a vulnerable child is exhausting because you need to remain hyper-vigilant, watching for every danger and threat. Managing Wayne meant always having to know where he was and what he was doing. Were any knives, matches or sharp tools lying around, phones for him to steal, or wallets from which he might take money? Were there any people around him with whom he might interact inappropriately, any younger children who might wind him up or who might be vulnerable if he joined in their play, which could then get out of hand?

There is no possibility of friends or family giving you a break because there is no one you know who can manage your child's behaviour. There is no one to whom you could admit that your child is a thief, a liar, someone with obsessive behaviours who may become violent if even the simplest thing goes wrong. You struggle 24 hours a day to live with your child and you can end up exhausted and depressed. You can see no hope for the future.

However, it is not all negative. We were able to take great pride in Wayne's achievements. At primary school, he took part in the swimming gala. In the Boys' Brigade, he was able to hold a constant beat on the bass drum to become part of the marching band. He is very caring, particularly with people who have a physical disability. He is very polite, with good manners. There have been so many things to celebrate, and he has brought a precious additional depth to our lives and those of his siblings, and his wider family.

How have we helped Wayne to gain the skills he needs for life?
When Wayne joined our family, we hoped that we would help him to catch up in his development and conform to our expectations of what, now at 25 years old, he should be achieving. We expected him to:

- make an attachment to us as his family;
- catch up with developmental experiences he had missed;
- learn enough at school to gain some qualifications;
- develop socially in order to build meaningful relationships;

- learn how to follow the normally accepted social rules;

- develop emotional literacy to understand his own and other people's responses to different situations;

- learn the difference between right and wrong;

- behave in a responsible way in order to keep on the right side of the law;

- learn self-care skills and apply them appropriately;

- learn how to manage and organise his time;

- control his impulses to acquire other people's belongings;

- be able to hold down a job;

- learn to live independently;

- have his own family in his own time, if that is his choice.

    We haven't managed to achieve what we hoped for, but Wayne certainly has benefited from being part of our family.

- He knows who his family is, and whenever he has a problem or if he needs an answer to a question, he will telephone us or ask his carers to contact us, or his brothers and sisters.

- He can now have a meal in a smart restaurant, enjoy leisure activities such as going swimming or to the cinema, and is accepted in social gatherings and family parties.

- He gained some basic qualifications at school and learnt many new skills at college.

- He completed school without a single day of formal exclusion.

- He has made friends, particularly from his residential college, some of whom he continues to meet on a regular basis.

- He knows the difference between right and wrong, although he still struggles to manage his impulse to do some things that are unacceptable.

- He has, with our support, managed to avoid getting a criminal record.

- He can now manage his personal hygiene, albeit that he needs reminders to keep to a routine.

- He is polite and has good manners, a key to socialising, which he loves.

- He is aware of people with physical disabilities and is the first to offer help.

- He can recognise anxiety in others and is able to offer comfort.

- He can find things to do to occupy himself (sometimes a little more inventive than we would like) and is usually willing to try new activities.

- He is able to hold down a simple job if he is properly supervised.

- He has created a life for himself away from his family.

Wayne will always need to live in a highly supervised environment, but is now able to make choices for himself, and he has the backing and support to have a good quality of life. If he hadn't come to live in our family, the plan for him was to be placed in a children's home, and it is unlikely that he would have had the quality of life he now enjoys.

What has helped us to parent Wayne and what has not?

We have been helped by the following things.

- Having a statement of special educational needs, which helped Wayne to access the learning support he needed to manage school.

- The label of "developmental delay" meant that we had high expectations, that enabled us to remain optimistic that his learning and behaviours would improve.

- Finding and reading the literature about attachment disorder and the effect of early abuse and trauma on brain development, which enabled us to understand our son, and helped us to stop being frustrated when he failed to learn what we were trying to teach him.

- Finding out about the nasal spray that sorted out the night bedwetting.

- Adoption conferences and adoption support groups, which enabled us to talk to other adoptive parents and realise that we were not alone in trying to manage developmental delay and challenging behaviours.

- Having a diagnosis and psychiatric report, which confirmed our understanding of our son's difficulties.

- Having detailed reports from the residential college, which gave us the evidence we needed to access the services Wayne required to support his transition to independence.

- Learning how to prepare risk assessments, which enabled us to demonstrate to the professionals what would happen if support was not provided.

However, some of our experiences have made our life more difficult.

- The label of "developmental delay", while encouraging us to hope, also gave us the unrealistic expectation that Wayne would eventually catch up rather more than has actually been possible.

- The lack of adoption support services left us feeling abandoned and impotent when faced with some of Wayne's most challenging behaviours, as did the professionals who refused to listen and understand the pressure we were under in trying to keep our son safe.

- Wayne's ability to hold social conversations hid his real difficulties and made it hard for those assessing him to see any real problems.

- Some assessments and reports made it look as if the problems our son had were due to our poor parenting.

- Other people's comments that Wayne would "grow out of it" and family friends who misunderstood his difficulties and were inclined to undermine our parenting strategies because they thought we were too protective.

- Those professionals who greeted our hopes with cynical dismissals: 'He needs this, but he doesn't fit our criteria....' (albeit we generally managed to prove otherwise).

Some golden rules

- Make sure that you get as much information as possible about your child's early history.

- Read as much as possible to help you to understand your child, what their behaviour means and what is covered by the term "developmental delay".

- Talk to other adopters to help you realise you are not alone.

SECTION II

- Keep a journal to remind you of the details of events. This helps to provide information when assessments are made, and over time you can see how your child is making progress.

- Remain optimistic as well as realistic about your child's progress.

- Ask for support, whether you are adopting or fostering.

- Approach it all with as much humour as you can muster: find and treasure the little gems of wonder in what may feel like a daily grind.

- Try to see through your child's eyes: you will understand better what is happening.

- Listen to your child.

- Involve the professionals in your child's care and get a diagnosis – but remember, children may have multiple conditions.

- Challenge any diagnosis about which you are unsure.

- Remember that you know your child better than the professionals, so stay strong and don't be fobbed off.

- Plan for the future – your journal will help to provide evidence to support your plans.

- Don't berate yourself if you make a mistake – you are doing better than anyone else could for your child.

- Don't be afraid to conclude that your child cannot handle a situation or experience, and have the confidence to pull them out of it.

- Look after yourself. Recognise the signs of exhaustion, secondary traumatic stress and depression, and don't be afraid to ask for help.

SECTION 11

- Take breaks: this isn't abandoning your child.

- Have fun being a parent and celebrate your child's every success. No matter how small you think a success is, it is massive for you and your child.

In conclusion

The bigger picture…our hope was not misplaced, and we continue to hold on to it, for Wayne, his siblings, and ourselves. Wayne has achieved far more than might have been expected, not just originally, but at every stage. He does have a widespread and restricting developmental delay, but has managed to temper its effects on his life. He can communicate, socialise, hold down a voluntary job, take care of his basic needs, and cook and care for others. This is a far cry from the wild child in nappies who, at nearly eight years old, could neither feed himself nor hold even a basic conversation.

Wayne has brought us many frustrations and heartaches, but also so much that is good and enriching. He sees the details we miss; he always looks to help; he wins people over with his generosity of spirit. "Wayne logic" has become the grounds for a wry smile at the shared bizarre situations into which it has led us. The treasures of parenting Wayne are the shared times of discovery during adventure holidays or outings, and the togetherness of family occasions. No: all in all, we have no regrets.

We now accept that Wayne can never achieve independent living, but we realise he can be happy and fulfilled without it. All of our children have come to us with degrees of developmental delay arising from their early experiences, before and after birth. It never ceases to amaze how diverse are those delays, and how diverse but still amazing are the youngsters' abilities to move on from those difficult starting positions.

Lisa's and Chris' problems and their progress to the present day were set out earlier in our story. The developmental delay of our other children spanned:

- educational gaps: not just being behind, but with fundamental learning difficulties;

- cause and effect thinking: the foundation of conscience, so a concerning gap if allowed to continue into adulthood;

- physical co-ordination and strength: as a result of pre-birth trauma; neglect in early years and, for some, the physical trauma of early years injury;

- emotional awareness: understanding their own feelings and those of others;

- emotional control, the ability to self-soothe, and to rationalise feelings.

For the most part, they have all progressed well. Some progress has been compromised by brain injuries or other inhibiting factors, but on the whole it has been possible for them, with help, to develop ways around these blockages. This underlines how important it is to hope, continuously to review, and to reframe. We have, together with our children, recognised their delays, and talked to them about their problems so that they can be part of the solution, but we have also wrapped them in experiences of parenting and family life that will help them to develop further.

This, then, is at the heart of parenting the child with developmental delay. You must have hope, and you must

89

set high expectations – realistic and constantly revisited and re-set, but high – because if you don't, nobody will.

Useful organisations

KIDS

An organisation working with disabled children, young people and their families across England. It offers a range of services for children with disabilities and developmental difficulties. For details of their regional offices, visit the website.

www.kids.org.uk

Contact a Family

An organisation that provides support, advice and information for families with disabled children, no matter what their situation or disability.

209–211 City Road
London EC1V 1JN
Tel: 020 7608 8700
Helpline: 0808 808 3555
www.cafamily.org.uk

If your child's developmental delay is associated with a specific condition such as learning disability, cerebral palsy or autism, one or more of the following organisations will be of use.

MENCAP

An organisation that supports people with learning disabilities and their families and carers. The helpline provides impartial advice on all learning disability issues for those living in England. MENCAP has offices in Wales and Northern Ireland – visit the website for more details.

123 Golden Lane
London EC1Y 0RT
Tel: 020 7454 0454
MENCAP Direct helpline: 0808 808 1111 (9am–5pm, Mon–Fri)
www.mencap.org.uk

Scope (England and Wales)

An organisation that supports people with cerebral palsy and their families and carers. For information on Scope's services, cerebral palsy or any aspect of living with disability, contact the Scope Response helpline, which offers confidential advice and information.

6 Market Road
London N7 9PW
Tel: 020 7619 7100
Scope Response helpline: 0808 800 3333 (9am–5pm, Mon–Fri)
www.scope.org.uk

Scope in Scotland

Capability Scotland
Head Office, Westerlea
11 Ellersly Road
Edinburgh EH12 6HY
Tel: 0131 337 9876
www.capability-scotland.org.uk

National Autistic Society

An organisation that supports people with an Autism Spectrum Disorder and their families and carers. The autism helpline provides impartial, confidential information, advice and support for people with autism spectrum disorders and their families and carers.
Tel: 0808 800 1050
Autism helpline: 0808 800 4104 (10am–4pm, Mon–Fri)
www.autism.org.uk

Education

For education advice, consult your local authority, or alternatively the Advisory Centre for Education (ACE) (www.ace-ed.org.uk/) or Independent Parental Special Needs Advice (IPSA) (**www.ipsea.org. uk/**, helpline: 0800 018 4016)

Health and mental health

Your GP should be able to refer you to relevant local health services such as paediatrics, speech and language therapy, occupational therapy and physiotherapy. There may be a local Child Development Team which brings together a number of these services.

Your GP should also be able to refer you to Child and Adolescent Mental Health Services (CAMHS) for help with emotional and behavioural issues in the child, help with parenting and for siblings who may be responding adversely to their sibling's developmental problems.

Financial advice

The organisations mentioned above will be able to advise you on what financial support you may be entitled to. Alternatively, contact your local FSSC (Family Support and Social Care Team – formerly Social Services) or your nearest Citizens Advice Bureau. You can also call the Benefits Enquiry Helpline on 0800 882200.